A Home Run for
PEANUTS

How Georgia's Peanut Farmers Fuel Active Kids

ISBN: 9798612757917

Published by the Georgia Peanut Commission, Tifton, Ga.

Book design by Tracy McMurphy
Produced by Hannah Jones on behalf of the Georgia Peanut Commission

To Tyler — you're the peanut butter to my jelly! - AR

To my kids --- dream big and do what you love! - MW

To Georgia's peanut farm families—your dedication and
commitment to producing a high-quality food for a hungry
world is an inspiration to all of us. - GPC

WINTER

Hey there! My name is Jake, and my family lives on a farm in Georgia. On our family farm, we raise chickens and cattle. We also grow corn, cotton, wheat, and my favorite — peanuts!

Have you ever visited a peanut farm before? No? Well, let's grab a peanut butter and jelly sandwich, and I'll show you around!

First, let's check out the shop. This is where we store our equipment to protect it from the weather. Every winter, I help my parents prep the machinery for the upcoming planting season. We grease the parts, change the oil, fill the tires, wash the windows and get everything ready for the big work the machinery will do throughout the year.

Who is nudging my hand, you ask? That's our farm dog, Max. He's really hairy and really friendly. If you give him a scratch behind the ears, he'll love you forever!

Max likes to hang out in the shop with us, but his favorite job is tagging along during planting season. I can't wait to get in the tractor this spring! When we head out to the field, you can come back and visit, okay?

I'll teach you the ropes!

See you at school!

Oh boy! It's the first day of spring, and it's time to get the field ready for planting!

But first, we've got to head to school. Mom made peanut butter protein bites for breakfast! They always give me extra energy to tackle the day, and they are delicious, too!

There's the bus! See you after school, Max!

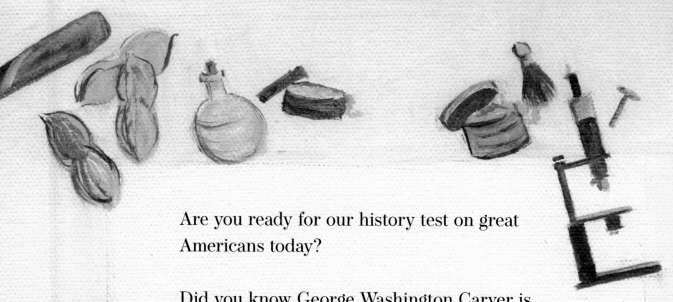

Are you ready for our history test on great Americans today?

Did you know George Washington Carver is considered the Grandfather of Peanuts? He was an inventor and discovered more than 300 uses for peanuts including rubber, glue, shampoo, shaving cream, linoleum, makeup and more! How cool is that?

Shh! The teacher says it's time to take our test. Max and I studied hard last night, so I think I'm ready.

Good luck!

Ring!!!

Whew! That was a tough test, but I think I aced it!

How about you?

The school bell rings, and class has ended for the day. It's time to head to baseball practice. The first game for our team, the Eagles, is coming soon, and I really need to work on my swing!

Let's play ball!

Now that practice is over, it's time to get to the farm. You're coming along, right? It's been a long day with school and sports, but our work on the family farm is just beginning.

Max is sure excited to see us! Did you miss us, boy? Friends, are you ready to help with peanut planting today? I'll teach you all the steps!

Let's go!

Planting is a two-step process.
Let me show you how it's done.

First, comes tilling. While we were at school, Dad turned the soil to ensure we have a good seedbed for the peanuts. We always wait to plant until the soil is warm. It's important the soil temperature is warm enough to sprout the seed and for the peanuts to grow.

Let's ride!

After tilling, the next step is placing the peanut seeds into the soil. A planter inserts each seed two inches deep and two inches apart in straight rows that span up and down the field. Once the peanuts are planted, we must be patient. It will take 120 to 150 days until the peanuts are fully grown.

Want to hop in a tractor and see how it's done? There's a buddy seat saved just for you!

SUMMER

School is out for the summer, and we have been busy tending to our crops. While we believe in working hard on the farm, don't worry — we make time for fun, too! For us, there's no better fun than family time at the baseball field!

Today is our first baseball game of the season! The Eagles are playing the Wildcats. The score is 8-8. I'm up at bat. The bases are loaded. There are two outs, so it's up to me to hit the ball and bring my teammates home for the win!

I step up to the plate. Mom and Dad are watching from the stands, eating peanuts and cheering me on.

As I grip the bat, I hear them cheer, "Go, Jake! You can do it!"

The first pitch comes in fast. I swing. I miss. The second is a curve ball. I miss again. I'm sweating bullets. My team is counting on me. The pitcher throws. It's a hard, low ball. I swing. I miss. Three strikes.

"You're out!" yells the umpire.

We lose the game. Oh no!

On the way home, I'm feeling pretty bummed. I let my team down, and I want to quit.

"Cheer up, Jake! You'll get them next time," says Mom.

"We'll keep working on your swing. Practice makes perfect," says Dad.

They remind me that playing baseball is a lot like farming. Sometimes, life throws you curveballs, and it's how you respond to those challenges that really makes a difference.

For example, farmers rely on sunshine and rain to help the peanuts grow. Too much or too little can hurt the plants. Even though the weather can be unpredictable at times, farmers work hard to ensure their peanut plants are healthy and strong throughout the year.

Likewise, I must practice my swing, so I can connect with any pitch coming my way! And you know what, I won't quit! The next time we play the Wildcats, I'll be ready.

Good morning! It's a new day on the farm, and it's time to head to the field.

Did you know peanut plants grow much differently than other plants? They don't grow on a bush or a tree. Instead, peanut plants flower above the ground while the fruit is found under the soil. Pretty cool, huh?

It's been a week since we planted the peanut seeds, and the plants are starting to crack out of the soil. Soon, they'll stand 18 inches tall.

In the next 30 to 40 days, yellow flowers will emerge and the plant will self-pollinate. As the petals dry out, a peanut ovary begins to form.

We call the budding peanut ovary, a "peg." As the peg grows, it forms a small stem with an embryo at the tip, which holds the peanut pod. Each pod holds the peanuts that we love to eat!

It all sounds pretty complicated, but us farmers have growing peanuts down to a science!

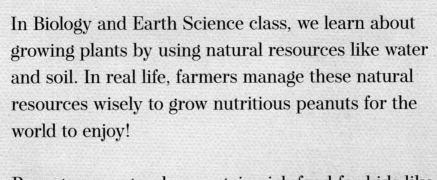

In Biology and Earth Science class, we learn about growing plants by using natural resources like water and soil. In real life, farmers manage these natural resources wisely to grow nutritious peanuts for the world to enjoy!

Peanuts are not only a protein-rich food for kids like us to eat, but they are good for the planet, too! Peanut plants efficiently use water, thanks to their deep root systems. Peanuts, also known as legumes, are nitrogen-fixing, which benefits both the plants and the soil without the need for fertilizers.

Peanuts are pretty awesome, if you really stop to think about it!

FALL

Now that we've learned about how peanuts grow, let's take a break and practice our baseball swing. I've been tossing up balls to hit every chance I get, and Max fetches them for me. It's pretty fun for both of us, and I think I've improved my swing a lot over the summer.

Our team has been undefeated since our loss to the Wildcats. Our last game of the season will soon be here. We'll once again face our rivals, and this time I'm going to be ready! Let's practice a bit more before we head into the house for supper.

I love family meals around the kitchen table. There's always lots of food and lots of laughter. Tonight, Dad is grilling steaks. Mom is making her famous strawberry, honey peanut salad. For dessert, we are having my favorite, peanut butter pie!

As we gather around the table, Dad says to me, "The peanut plants will be ready to harvest soon, Jake."

"The university's county agent tested the peanuts for us today," adds Mom. "He says the plants have grown thick and fruitful. That is a sure sign harvest time is near."

Harvesting is so much fun! I can't wait for you to see!

Rise and shine! It's harvest time! I'm glad you're here to see all of the action!

Just like planting, harvesting peanuts is a two-step process.

First, Dad drives a machine called a "digger" along the peanut rows. The digger's job is to dig the peanut plant, shake off the dirt, flip it upside down and set it back down on the row to dry.

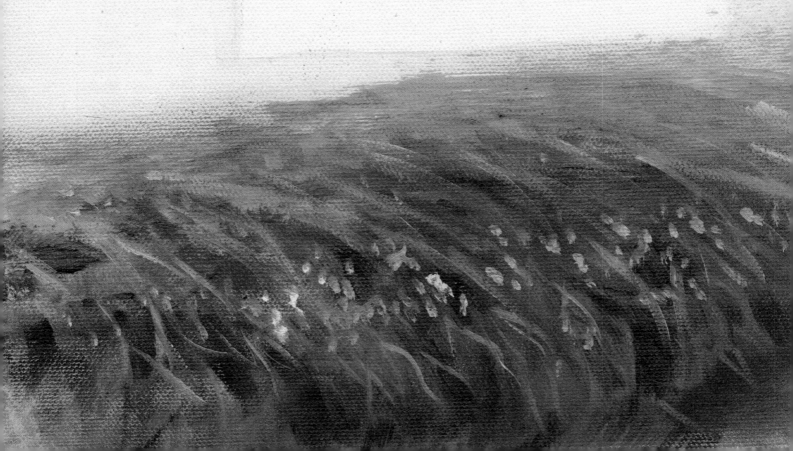

Next, after the peanuts dry in the field for a few days, we use a second machine called a "combine" to separate the peanut pods from the rest of the plant.

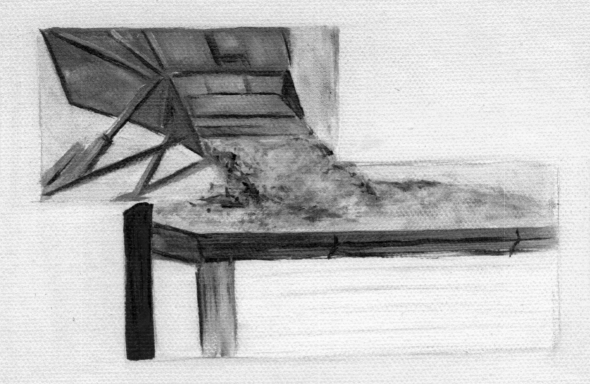

Once the peanuts have been harvested, we haul them in a wagon or semi-trailer to a buying point, where they are tested, cleaned, dried and stored. Once they are taken out of storage, they are processed to be sold in grocery stores as roasted peanuts, peanut butter and so much more!

Now that harvest is complete, our work on the farm is done for the season. Let's head to our final baseball game of the year!

Today's game is the Eagles against the Wildcats, and it's my chance to redeem myself after I struck out to lose our first game of the year.

As we stand for the National Anthem before the game, my nerves are at an all-time high. However, I've been practicing with Max every chance I get. Mom and Dad say I've got a really mean swing, and I'm ready. I can do this. I know I can!

"Let's play ball!" yells the umpire.

The game is an exciting one. The Wildcats are good, but we are good, too. Our practice has paid off, but can we win the game?

The score is tied. I'm the last up to bat. I'm determined this time. I walk confidently up to the plate. I position my feet just right and square my shoulders. I tighten my grip on the bat.

"Swing hard, Jake! Give it all you've got!" yells Dad.

"We believe in you," says Mom.

I nod to the pitcher. He throws me a fast curve ball. I swing with all my might, and I hear the clink of the bat as the ball goes flying.

I drop my bat and run, and my baseball coach cries out, "Going, going, gone! It's a home run for Jake!"

I round the bases while the crowd goes wild! The Eagles win the game, and we finish the season strong!

To celebrate, Mom and Dad invite the whole team, all of the parents and our coaches back to the farm for a cookout! We've got hamburgers, hotdogs, potato salad, corn-on-the cob and a fan favorite — chocolate peanut butter cookies!

As the baseball season officially ends for the year, our next farming season is just beginning. It's time to plant our winter wheat crop. We will move the peanut equipment back to the shop until next year when we start the process all over again.

Just like on the baseball field where we work hard to improve and win games, farmers work hard every day to improve the soil, take care of the land and produce a home run crop of nutritious peanuts to feed the world!

A home run won the game for our team,
and on the farm and in the kitchen, it's always

a home run for peanuts!

Buddy seat — Tractors typically have one seat for the driver and a second smaller seat for a passenger. This is often referred to as the "buddy seat."

Buying point — A purchasing location for farmers to take their harvested peanut crop to. Once delivered, peanuts are received, weighed, cleaned, dried, inspected, graded and prepared for storage and shelling.

Combine — A complex farm machine that performs the processes of reaping, threshing and cleaning.

County agent — A university expert; employed through the Extension service who advises farmers on production and marketing technique and to promote educational programs fitted to the needs of rural people.

Digger — A heavy-duty machine that lifts peanuts from the soil, separates pods from the soil, elevates the vine mass, inverts and windrows the vines and exposes the pods to the air for curing.

Embryo — The origin of the plant, where the seed grows and produces a flowering plant.

Fertilizers — A chemical or natural substance added to the land to increase its fertility and promote soil health.

Harvest — In the fall, ripe crops are cut, collected, dried and stored.

GLOSSARY

Legume — Edible seeds, which grow together in enclosed pods on a plant that fixes its own nitrogen.

Nitrogen-fixing — Growing peanuts promotes soil health as peanuts take nitrogen from the air and "fix" it into the soil through their root systems.

Peanut ovary — As the embryo begins the process for the peanut to grow, the ovary holds and ripens into a pod that contains one to three oily, edible peanut seeds.

Peg — The budding peanut ovary, which grows down into the soil. The tip of the ovary contains the mature peanut pod.

Pods — A peanut pod develops underground from the stem of the peg. The mature peanuts will ripen beneath the surface of the soil and will be dug up at harvest time.

Seedbed — A bed of fine soil in which seedlings are germinated.

Soil — The upper layer of dirt in which plants grow that consists of a mixture of organic matter, clay and rock particles.

Tilling — To prepare and cultivate land for crops by breaking up and turning over the soil.

Winter wheat — Wheat sown in fall or winter for harvesting the following summer.

Game Day Peanut Butter Protein Bites

Ingredients:

3 cups quick oats

½ cup dried cranberries

½ cup chopped peanuts

½ cup butter

¾ cup honey

2/3 cup brown sugar

1 cup peanut butter

1 teaspoon vanilla

Directions:

Lightly spray an 8" baking sheet with non-stick spray or line it with parchment paper.

If using a stove-top: In a bowl, mix together oats, cranberries and nuts. Melt butter in a large, heavy bottomed saucepan. Mix in honey and brown sugar to bring to a boil over medium-high heat. Boil and stir for 2 ½ minutes. Remove from heat. Working quickly, stir in the peanut butter and vanilla until blended, then thoroughly mix in the oat mixture. Roll the mixture into 1.5-inch balls and let cool completely. Cool and serve.

If using a microwave: In a bowl, mix together oats, cranberries and peanuts and set aside. Next, stir the butter, honey, peanut butter and brown sugar in a microwave safe bowl. Heat in 30 second increments, stirring in between, until the mixture is combined and pourable. Add vanilla to honey and peanut butter mixture and stir. Then, add honey and peanut butter mixture to dry ingredients, stirring quickly to combine. Roll the mixture into 1.5-inch balls and let cool completely. Cool and serve.

Meet the Georgia Peanut Commission

The Georgia Agricultural Commodity Commission for Peanuts was established in 1961 under the Commodities Promotion Act. The Commission conducts programs in the areas of promotion, research and education. Funding is derived from a $2 per ton assessment on all producers. Governing the Commission is a five-man elected board of peanut farmers. "A Home Run for Peanuts" is a project of the Georgia Peanut Commission. Supplemental materials and lesson plans can be found at www.gapeanuts.com.

Meet the Ag Storytellers

We are a team of agricultural professionals and moms who are on a mission to tell agriculture's rich stories through accurate, engaging and vibrant children's books that will become a favorite on the bookshelf, as well as a legacy for the producers we represent. With decades of combined experience in the areas of writing, illustrating and design, Ag Storytellers is a collaborative effort that connects consumers with producer.

Meet the author, Amanda Radke. She is a seasoned agricultural journalist, blogger for BEEF Magazine, children's book author, international speaker and cattle rancher, based in South Dakota. She holds a degree in Agricultural Communications, Education and Leadership from South Dakota State University. With extensive media training, consumer advocacy experience and years of reading children's books at elementary schools and libraries, Amanda works to create a dynamic storyline that will capture the attention of young readers while accurately representing the experiences of farmers/ranchers.

Meet the illustrator, Michelle Weber. She is an author, illustrator, ranch wife and artist, located in Minnesota. She specializes in agricultural and livestock art. Weber has built her portfolio on a national and international level, selling her work to 36+ states, Canada, Europe, Australia and Asia. With a degree from South Dakota State University in Advertising, Marketing and Sociology, Michelle not only brings unique design and perspective to every illustration on canvas, but she also understands how the visual impact will influence and inspire readers.

Meet the designer, Tracy McMurphy. She is a graphic designer and online marketing specialist, as well as the owner of the Red Angus World and a beef cattle producer from Texas. McMurphy holds a bachelor's degree in Agricultural Communications from Oklahoma State and a master's degree in Mass Communication from the Cronkite School of Journalism at Arizona State University. With each project, McMurphy pulls the elements of the book together to create a gorgeous published product that will be a legacy on the bookshelf for years to come.

Meet the Ag Storytellers

Amanda Radke
Author

Michelle Weber
Illustrator

Tracy McMurphy
Designer

AG Storytellers

PROMOTING AGRICULTURAL LITERACY THROUGH
ACCURATE, ENGAGING AND VIBRANT BOOKS FOR KIDS.

To learn more about Ag Storytellers, visit our website.
WWW.AGSTORYTELLERS.COM

Made in the USA
Monee, IL
16 February 2020